GRAPHIC SCIENCE

ADVENTURES IN SOUND

with MAX AXIOM SUPER SCIENTIST

Emily Sohn

illustrated by Cynthia Martin and Anne Timmons

Raintree

www.raintreepublishers.co.uk
Visit our website to find out
more information about
Raintree books.

To order:
☎ Phone +44 (0) 1865 888066
🖹 Fax +44 (0) 1865 314091
💻 Visit www.raintreepublishers.co.uk

Raintree is an imprint of Capstone Global Library Limited, a company incorporated in England and
Wales having its registered office at 7 Pilgrim Street, London EC4V 6LB
Registered company number: 6695882

ISBN 978 1 406 21455 0 (hardback)   ISBN 978 1 406 21471 0 (paperback)
14 13 12 11 10   15 14 13 12 11

British Library Cataloguing in Publication Data
Sohn, Emily
Sound. -- (Graphic science)
534-dc22
A full catalogue record for this book is available from the British Library.

Art Director and Designer: Bob Lentz
Cover Artist: Tod Smith
Colourist: Michael Kelleher
UK Editor: Diyan Leake
UK Production: Alison Parsons
Originated by Capstone Global Library
Printed and bound in China by South China Printing Company Limited

Acknowledgements
The publisher would like to thank the following for permission to reproduce copyright material:
Capstone Press, 8 bottom (Scott Thoms)

Disclaimer
All the Internet addresses (URLs) given in this book were valid at the time of going to press.
However, due to the dynamic nature of the Internet, some addresses may have changed, or sites may
have changed or ceased to exist since publication. While the publisher regrets any inconvenience this
may cause readers, no responsibility for any such changes can be accepted by the publisher.

CONTENTS

Do you see that? Vibrations cause invisible waves in the air, the way that throwing a pebble in a pond causes ripples in the water. These waves make up what we call sound.

SUBJECT: JACKHAMMER

SOUND WAVES

When an object vibrates, it actually causes nearby air molecules to bounce against each other.

SUBJECT: JACKHAMMER

Their motion causes other molecules to bounce too. This transfer of energy moves outward from the source of the sound, creating sound waves.

MOLECULES: Tiny particles that make up a substance

Of course, some sounds are louder than others. The difference is called intensity.

TWEET!
TWEET!
TWEET!

TATATATATAT!

Stronger vibrations are more intense. They cause louder sounds.

Loudness is also called volume. The higher the volume, the louder the sound.

PUTT
PUTT
PUTT

IDLE ON OFF

I have a job to do. Please, leave me alone.

PUTT
PUTT
PUTT
PUTT

THE HUMAN LARYNX

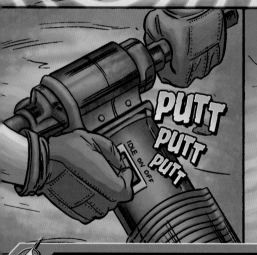

EPIGLOTTIS
VOCAL CORDS
LARYNX
TRACHEA

Inside your throat, your larynx allows you to talk, sing, and make other noises. Inside the larynx, two muscles called vocal cords squeeze together and vibrate as air passes by them. The faster they vibrate, the higher your voice sounds. Your tongue and lips shape the sounds you make.

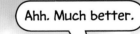

Distance affects volume, too. Sound waves lose energy as they travel. So, the farther away I get, the quieter the drill sounds to me.

Ahh. Much better.

TWEET!
TWEET!

There is more to sound than just volume. That bird's song gets louder and softer, but it is also full of notes, some higher than others.

The bird may not know it, but the secrets behind its lovely melody are called frequency and pitch.

Frequency equals the number of sound waves that pass a point during a certain amount of time.

For instance, right now only one sound wave passes by me each second. Therefore, the sound has a frequency of 1 hertz (Hz).

One Second

But if 50 waves pass by me in one second, the sound has 50 Hz. Faster vibrations create sounds with higher frequencies.

One Second

We've gone to the source of sound waves. Now, let's take a look at how these invisible waves turn into the sounds we hear.

Noise, noise. Who do these people think they are?

We hear through our ears, so let's take a look inside Al's ear.

Believe it or not, the folds and curves of the outer ear serve a purpose.

They collect sounds and funnel them into the ear.

OUTER EAR

MIDDLE EAR

INNER EAR

The ear canal is also part of the outer ear. It carries sounds to the middle ear just ahead.

WAX

EAR DRUM

HAMMER

ANVIL

In the middle ear, sounds vibrate the eardrum and three tiny bones called the hammer, anvil, and stirrup.

STIRRUP

Together, these parts make sounds louder before they are sent into the inner ear.

Vibrations from the stirrup travel to the snail-shaped cochlea in the inner ear.

Liquid in the cochlea gets wavy when vibrations arrive.

COCHLEA

These are hair cells inside the cochlea. They send electrical signals to the brain. The signals serve as messages that sound has arrived.

TO BRAIN

HAIR CELLS

YAK! YAK! YAK! YAK! YAK!!

Sound moves pretty fast. But how fast is it?

The speed of sound depends on what sound travels through.

Sound travelling through air at sea level and room temperature moves at 1240 kilometres, or 770 miles, per hour.

1240 KPH

SOUND VERSUS LIGHT

ACCESS GRANTED: MAX AXIOM

In a race, light would leave sound in the dust. Nothing moves faster than light, which zings along at about 1,080,000,000 kilometres (670,000,000 miles) per hour.

Whew!

Hee! Hee!

BOOM!

We can't travel faster than light, but we can move faster than the speed of sound.

That supersonic jet just broke the sound barrier. When it did, it left a whole bunch of sound waves in its wake. The sound waves piled up and produced a sonic boom.

That boom was loud. But it was different from the sharp jarring noise of the jackhammer.

BARNACLE BOB'S DIVE BOATS

Every sound is different, and lots of factors affect whether something sounds quiet or muffled, loud or shrill.

Let's find out why.

BBLUUUUWW

The material sound travels through affects how you hear it.

Yikes!

Hi, Max! Did you know that sound waves travel five times faster through water than through air?

If you've ever listened to sounds underwater, you may know what I mean.

Oh, yeah. It's also hard to tell which direction sounds are coming from underwater. That whale really took me by surprise!

It was probably talking to other whales. Many creatures use sound to communicate underwater.

That's cool! But I think I'll try to find someplace quieter.

It's so quiet in space. I can't even hear you pounding on the space station.

I wanted quiet, but this is ridiculous!

That's because space is a vacuum. There's no air. Sound needs some type of material to travel through.

So, if our radios quit working, we'd have no way to talk to each other?

Not unless we pressed our helmets together and let the sound of our voices pass between the plastic visors.

Wow! I think I'll head back to Earth where I can talk as much as I want.

Besides air and water, sound can travel through solids too.

These kids can hear each other talk into the cups because the string vibrates and carries sound waves between them.

Now we know where sounds come from and how we hear them. Let's check out what sound can do and what we can do with sound.

RRUMMBLE!

RRUMBLE!

CRACKK!

RUMBLE!

RUMBLE!

Uh, oh. There's a storm coming. Time to head indoors.

I'll just hop on this sound wave and take it for a ride.

Sound waves don't always travel in a straight line. Water can bend, or refract, a sound wave. That's because sound changes direction when it goes from air to water.

I know an oceanographer who uses sound to study the ocean floor. Let's see what he's up to today.

Sonar is a great tool. Whoever came up with the idea must have been pretty smart.

That's true, but animals figured it out first.

Many animals use sonar to find prey and avoid predators. When bats do it, it's called echolocation. Rats, whales, and dolphins also get information from bouncing sound waves.

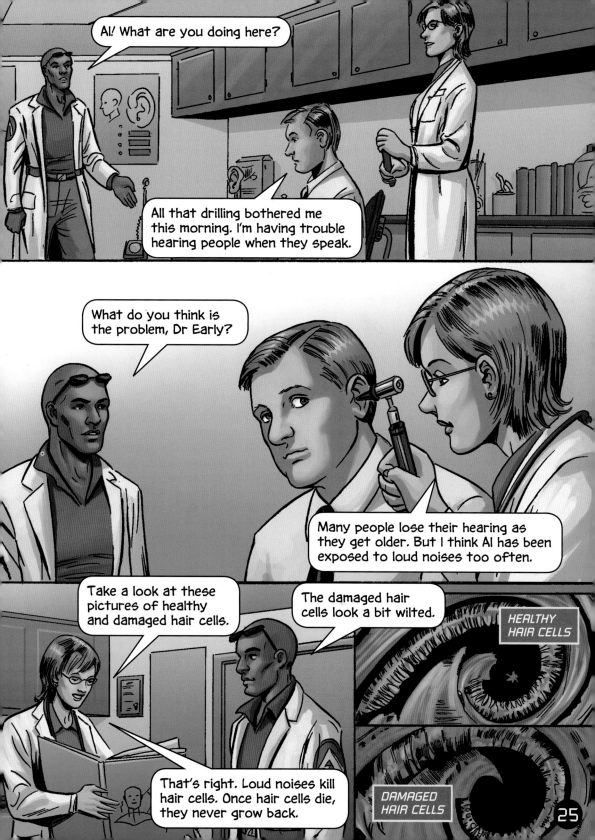

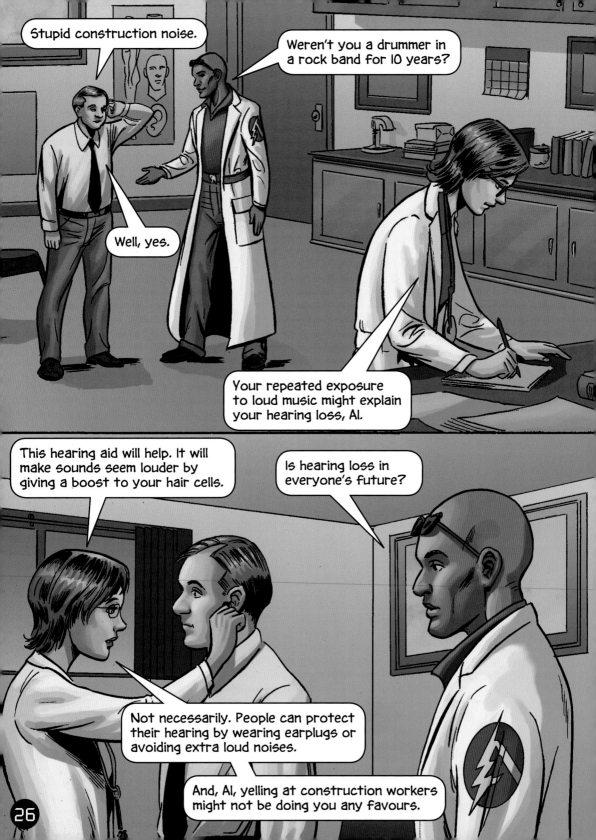

MORE ABOUT SOUND

Sound travels faster through solids than through gases and liquids. Why? Because the molecules in solids are packed closer together. The closer the molecules, the faster the sound waves travel from one molecule to the next. A sound travels 1,240 kilometres (770 miles) per hour through air. It speeds through steel at about 18,716 kilometres (11,630 miles) per hour.

Most bats use echolocation to hunt. As they fly, bats release high-pitched sounds that bounce off objects all around them. The bats use the echoes they hear to locate and determine the size of insects fluttering nearby.

The hammer, anvil, and stirrup are the smallest bones in the human body. They are the same size now as they were the day you were born. All together, they could fit on a penny.

Ear wax helps keep your ears clean. As wax forms inside the ear canal, it clings to dirt particles. Eventually, the wax works its way out of the ear, carrying the dirt along with it.

The liquid in the cochlea does more than just magnify vibrations. It also plays a role in balance and helps your body know what is up and what is down.

Elephants use infrasound, or sound below the range of human hearing, to talk to each other. They can use rumbling sounds as low as 5 Hz to communicate.

A cricket's hearing organs are located just below the knees of its front legs. A cicada's hearing organ is on its abdomen.

Scientists measure the loudness, or volume, of sounds in decibels (dB). A whisper measures about 20 dB, while normal talking is 60 dB. A jet measures about 120 dB and a firecracker exploding is about 140 dB. Any sound above 85 dB can cause hearing damage if listened to for too long. At close range, noise levels above 140 dB cause immediate hearing damage.

Blue whales are the loudest animals on earth. Their calls have measured 188 dB and can be heard from hundreds of miles away.

MORE ABOUT

SUPER SCIENTIST

Real name: Maxwell Axiom
Height: 1.86 m (6ft 1 in.)
Weight: 87 kg (13 st. 10 lb.)
Eyes: Brown   Hair: None

Super capabilities: Super intelligence; able to shrink to the size of an atom; sunglasses give X-ray vision; lab coat allows for travel through time and space.

Origin: Since birth, Max Axiom seemed destined for greatness. His mother, a marine biologist, taught her son about the mysteries of the sea. His father, a nuclear physicist and volunteer park warden, showed Max the wonders of the earth and sky.

One day, while Max was hiking in the hills, a megacharged lightning bolt struck him with blinding fury. When he awoke, he discovered a new-found energy and set out to learn as much about science as possible. He travelled the globe studying every aspect of the subject. Then he was ready to share his knowledge and new identity with the world. He had become Max Axiom, Super Scientist.

Glossary

absorb soak up

cochlea spiral-shaped part of the ear that helps send sound messages to the brain

decibel unit for measuring the volume of sounds

eardrum thin piece of skin stretched tight like a drum inside the ear; the eardrum vibrates when sound waves strike it.

echolocation the process of using sounds and echoes to locate objects. Bats use echolocation to find food.

energy ability to do work, such as moving things or giving heat or light

frequency the number of sound waves that pass a location in a certain amount of time

hertz unit for measuring the frequency of sound wave vibrations. One hertz equals one sound wave per second.

molecule two or more atoms of the same or different elements that have bonded. A molecule is the smallest part of a compound that can be divided without a chemical change.

pitch highness or lowness of a sound; low pitches have low frequencies and high pitches have high frequencies.

reflect bounce off an object

refract bend when passing through a material at an angle

vibration fast movement back and forth